Favorite Hymns BOOK THREE

Arranged by Deborah Brady

Contents

ISBN-10: 0-8497-9754-3
ISBN-13: 978-0-8497-9754-5

© 2009 La Jolla Music Company, Neil A. Kjos Music Company, Distributor, 4382 Jutland Drive, San Diego, California 92117.
International copyright secured. All rights reserved. Printed in U.S.A.

Just as I Am

Charlotte Elliott

William B. Bradbury
Arranged by Deborah Brady

4

Student plays one octave higher than written when playing with duet.

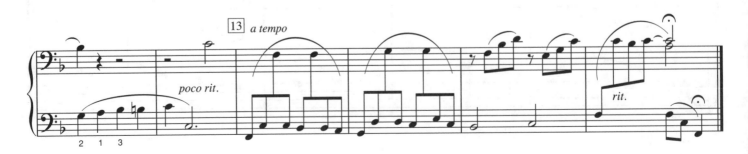

God, Who Made the Earth and Heaven

Reginald Heber

Traditional Welsh Melody
Arranged by Deborah Brady

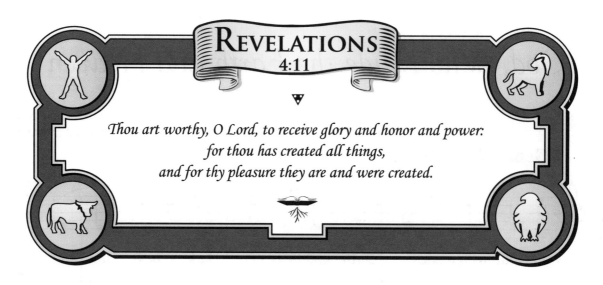

All Hail the Power of Jesus' Name!

Edward Perronet, alt.

Oliver Holden
Arranged by Deborah Brady

Come, Thou Almighty King

Anonymous

Felice de Giardini
Arranged by Deborah Brady

PSALM
36:8-9

*They shall be richly satisfied with the abundance of thy house;
and thou shalt make them drink of the river of thy pleasures.
For with thee is the fountain of life: in thy light shall we see light.*

Come, Thou Fount of Every Blessing

Robert Robinson

American Folk Tune
Arranged by Deborah Brady

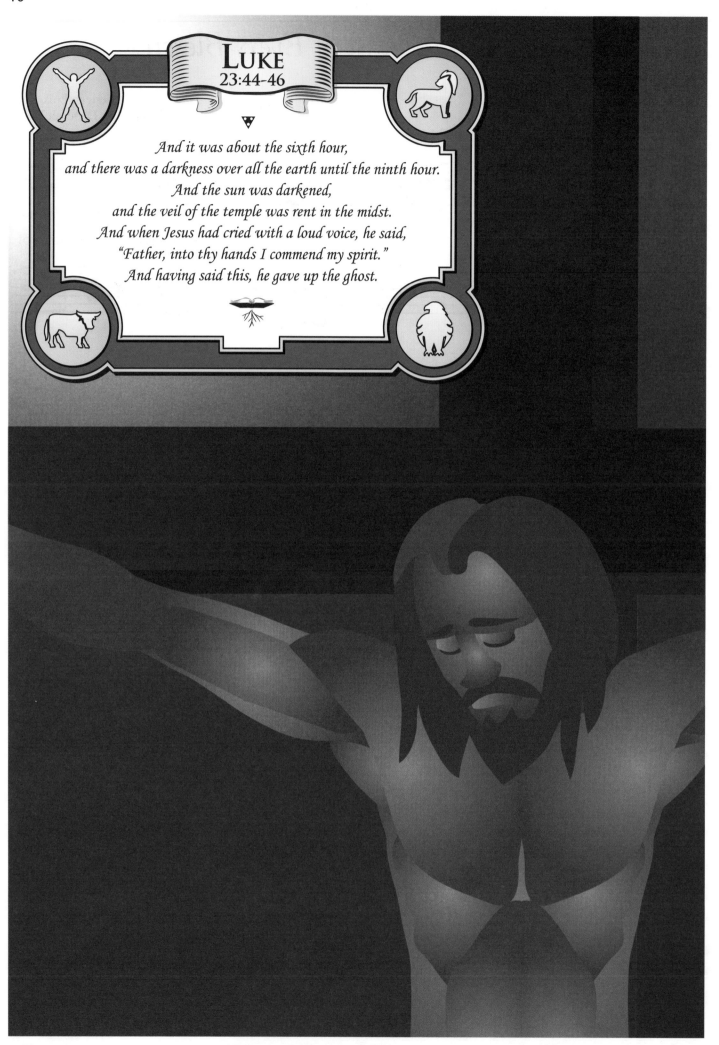

LUKE
23:44-46

*And it was about the sixth hour,
and there was a darkness over all the earth until the ninth hour.
And the sun was darkened,
and the veil of the temple was rent in the midst.
And when Jesus had cried with a loud voice, he said,
"Father, into thy hands I commend my spirit."
And having said this, he gave up the ghost.*

Were You There

American Spiritual
Arranged by Deborah Brady

PSALM
86:5

For thou, O Lord, art good,
and ready to forgive;
and plenteous in mercy
unto all who call upon thee.

There's a Wideness in God's Mercy

Frederick W. Faber

Dutch Melody
Arranged by Deborah Brady

This Is My Father's World

Maltbie D. Babcock

Traditional English Melody
Arranged by Deborah Brady

Holy, Holy, Holy! Lord God Almighty

Reginald Heber

John B. Dykes
Arranged by Deborah Brady

Abide with Me

Henry F. Lyte

William H. Monk
Arranged by Deborah Brady